GRAPHING AS AN AID TO CONCEPTUALIZATION IN APPLICATIONS

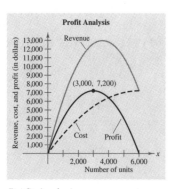

Profit Analysis

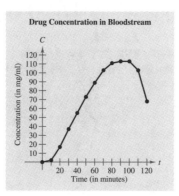

Fitting a Model to Data

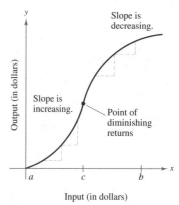

Point of Diminishing Returns

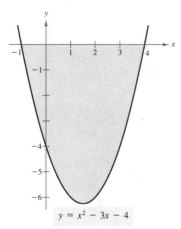

Area Between Two Graphs

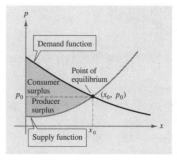

Consumer and Producer Surplus

CASE STUDIES

Study smarter!

Changing the way you study can help you earn better grades in your calculus course. Review the topics you need most, practice, and be ready.

The **Student Solutions Guide** (0-669-35167-9). This useful guide features:
• Detailed solutions to all the odd-numbered exercises in your text
• Practice tests with solutions for each chapter
• Study strategies

Looking for help with a graphing calculator?

If your instructor recommends graphing technology, the **Graphing Technology Keystroke Guide** (0-669-35169-5) will help you learn to use it. This specially designed guide includes keystrokes, screen displays, programs, and technology tips for BestGrapher software and several popular graphing calculator models, including:
• TI-81, TI-82, TI-85
• Casio fx-7700G, fx-9700GE, fx-7700GE
• Sharp EL 9200/9300
• Hewlett-Packard 48G- 48GX

Visualize math with BestGrapher software.

This powerful yet inexpensive software for MS-DOS and Macintosh makes it easy for you to see and understand mathematical concepts. With BestGrapher you can:

• Simultaneously display an equation, graph, and table of values
• Estimate zeroes and the intersections of curves
• Find and graph derivatives; perform numerical integration
• Draw tangent and secant lines
• Trace curves and display the coordinates at each point
• Zoom in to view more detail and zoom out to view a more complete graph
• Rescale, resize, and print the graphs you've created

Look for these supplements in your bookstore.

If you don't find them, check with your bookstore manager or call D. C. Heath toll free at 1-800-334-3284. In Canada, call toll free at 1-800-268-2472. Shipping, handling, and state tax may be added where applicable (tell the operator you are placing a #1-PREFER order).

BRIEF CALCULUS

with Applications

FOURTH EDITION